Aldsluf F.

A SEA SERPENT
The story of a nothosaur

BEVERLY HALSTEAD D.Sc.
(Reader in Geology and Zoology, Reading University)

pictures by
JENNY HALSTEAD

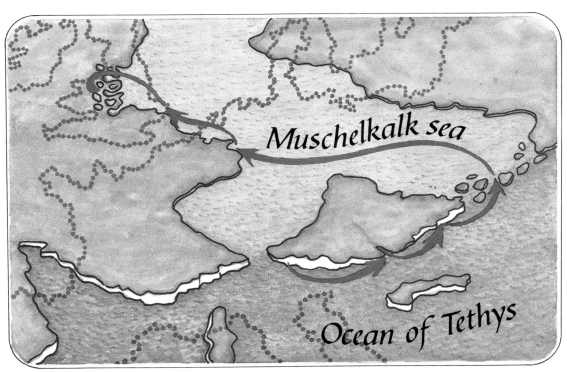

→ Andrian's journey 215 million years ago
▭ Land in Triassic times   ••••• Europe today

COLLINS

For Danny and Katie

William Collins Sons & Co Ltd
London · Glasgow · Sydney · Auckland
Toronto · Johannesburg

First published 1984
© text Beverly Halstead 1984
© illustrations Jenny Halstead 1984
ISBN 0 00 104123-1
Printed in Hong Kong by South China Printing Co.

Introduction

During what is known as the Triassic period, 215 million years ago, and 25 million years before brontosaurs roamed the Earth, all the land on Earth was joined together in one huge continent. To the east lay the ancient ocean of Tethys which stretched from what is now France to Japan.

Living at this time were sea reptiles which, although their young were born on land, spent much of their lives in water. Their remains have been found over a wide area along the shores of the ocean of Tethys. They were first found in southern Germany in a shelly limestone known as the Muschelkalk which had been deposited at the bottom of a clear, warm sea during the Middle Triassic period. There is also evidence that they reached England when for a very brief period the Muschelkalk Sea spread northwest and shallow lagoons formed in the desert area.

The first detailed description of these swimming reptiles was given in 1855 by Hermann von Meyer who described several different kinds, including *Nothosaurus andriani*. Nothosaurs grew to about 4 metres in length. They had a long skull with a pointed jaw carrying rows of sharp teeth, ideally suited for catching fish. The swimming tail carried a dorsal fin and their feet were clawed and webbed. They were powerful swimmers and also moved fairly easily on land. In this book we have followed the life of one nothosaur whom we have called Andrian.

A mother nothosaur retreated to the back of a deep sea-cave which opened on to a vast ocean, and there she gave birth to nine tiny nothosaurs. Within moments of giving birth, the mother left her young to go fishing. On her return, she regurgitated partly-digested fish which the young ones hastily gobbled up.

After only a few days the young nothosaurs were able to scramble towards the sea which filled the cave opening, but whenever they sensed danger they scuttled back to the safety of the dark interior. Soon they learnt to snap up the sand hoppers among the seaweed, and to catch small fish in pools left behind by the tide.

The discovery in a marine deposit in the Tessin Alps in Switzerland of a complete adult nothosaur surrounded by seven young, each about 25 cm long, suggests that nothosaurs gave birth to live young. In addition, young nothosaurs and large fish heads have been found in a fossilized Triassic sea-cave in Poland, indicating that nothosaurs cared for their offspring.

When the young nothosaurs were about a week old they ventured out of the cave with their parents and went fishing along the coast. The sea was warm and waves broke on the rocks at the foot of the cliffs. Shoals of fish were identified by gliding pterosaurs, *Eudimorphodon*, which swooped down to the water to snatch fish in their toothed beaks. The adult nothosaurs swept up several fish in their strong jaws, crunched them and then released them back into the water so that Andrian and the other youngsters could easily catch them.

> The first pterosaurs *Eudimorphodon* appeared in the Triassic period. They seem to have been sea-shore dwellers and fish-eaters.

The nothosaurs spent many hours basking in the sunshine on the rocks, flopping into the sea from time to time to catch fish and to cool off. One day a carnivorous reptile, the dinosaur ancestor, *Ticinosuchus* prowled onto the shore. Andrian, sunning himself on the rocks, suddenly spotted the hungry creature creeping towards them. He flung himself into the sea and his brothers and sisters, woken by the commotion, followed. *Ticinosuchus* pounced, but the nothosaurs escaped and swam round the headland to the next bay.

The *Ticinosuchus* is the only fully land reptile that has been found in rocks in Switzerland and Poland where nothosaurs have also been found.

Here the water seemed warmer and calmer and the nothosaurs dived and swam, catching fish and eating them. Suddenly danger threatened as the sea-lizard *Askeptosaurus* flashed through the water. Its long, whip-like tail propelled it at high speed towards the nothosaurs who scattered, making for the rocks. Andrian leapt out of the sea to escape the snapping jaws. But one of his brothers was not so fortunate.

The discovery of the marine sea-serpent *Askepto-saurus* in nothosaur-bearing rocks was the first evidence that lizards existed 215 million years ago.

Andrian and his brothers and sisters were now independent of their parents and they moved along the coast till they came to a wide estuary. Here the group of nothosaurs lived an easy life until they were almost fully grown. As the tide flooded the muddy banks it brought in plenty of fish. The nothosaurs walked easily over the mud on their webbed feet to catch horseshoe crabs and at night they slept among the roots of the trees. Occasionally an armoured, flesh-eating phytosaur swam into the estuary, but they could see it approaching and moved away.

Nothosaur fossils have been found in rocks which give evidence of a large river entering a muddy estuary. Their footprints show they had webbed feet. In similar rocks horseshoe crabs and dragonflies are preserved. Fossilized plant remains show primitive conifers with mangrove-like prop roots.

As the young nothosaurs grew they ventured more and more frequently back to the rocky coast to fish and dive. One day, Andrian, having caught a large lobster, crawled up on to the rocks to crack open the shell and eat the flesh. Surrounding him was a group of lizards, *Tanystropheus*. They had enormously long necks and as they sat on the rocks they dipped their heads into the sea to snatch up fish. Occasionally some of them slithered down into the water to swim. Andrian could find few fish among these creatures so he swam further out to sea.

For many years scientists were puzzled by the long neck bones of **Tanystropheus** and thought they must be the wing bones of a flying reptile. It was only when a complete skeleton was discovered in the Tessin Alps that they realised that **Tanystropheus** had a neck up to three metres long. Lobsters and prawns, similar to those around today, are found in Triassic rocks in Germany.

As he swam, he encountered a shoal of ammonites cruising through the water with their tentacles trailing. Andrian dived among them and grabbed one in his jaws. He bit hard on the shell and was suddenly engulfed in a cloud of black ink. He seized another but it wrapped its tentacles round his head and he was forced to let it go. The rest of the shoal had now swum away, propelled by jets of water which they shot out behind them.

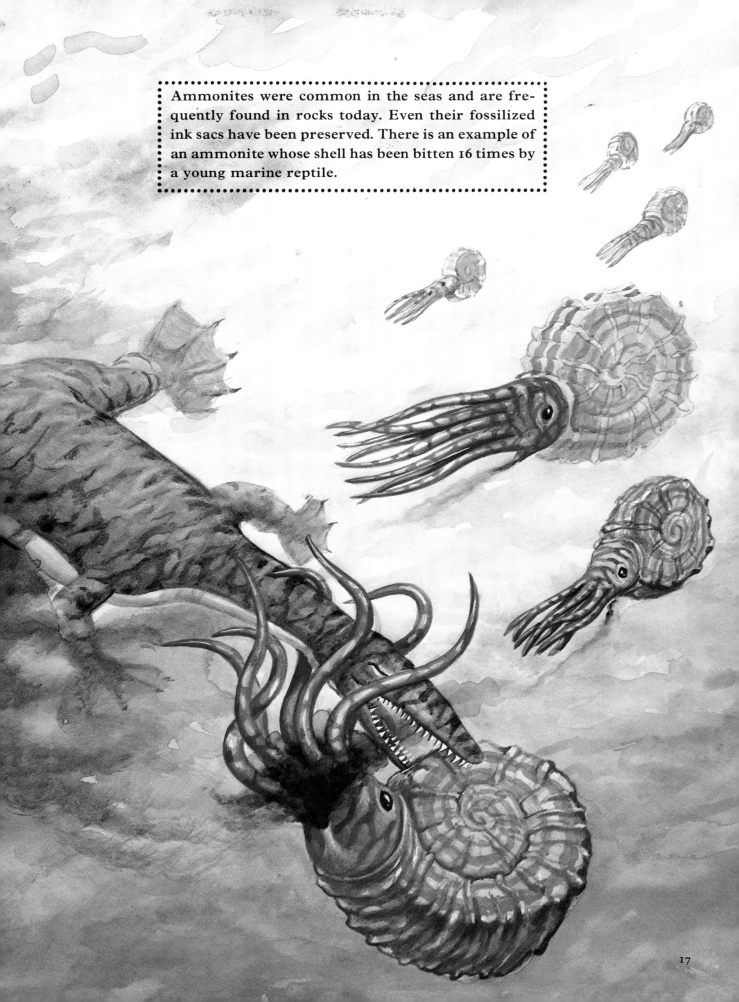

Ammonites were common in the seas and are frequently found in rocks today. Even their fossilized ink sacs have been preserved. There is an example of an ammonite whose shell has been bitten 16 times by a young marine reptile.

Andrian settled on a part of the coast which was already occupied by a large nothosaur colony. He scrambled onto the rocks and lay in the sun.

Eventually, he and one of the females in the colony mated, and they took over a cave where their litter of young was born. For the next few months the two parents were busy hunting for food for their growing family. They continually guarded their small offspring from the toothed pterosaurs which swooped down to snatch up young nothosaurs.

There is an abundance of nothosaur remains preserved in near-shore deposits in the Tessin Alps, and sea-caves in Poland. As these include large numbers of young ones it suggests a breeding place.

When Andrian and his mate were catching fish with their family, they came across a group of newly-born ichthyosaurs, *Mixosaurus*. Andrian and his mate gave chase but the mother *Mixosaurus* turned, and with her long, sharp-toothed snout struck at Andrian ripping the skin across his face and lashing him with her tail. The nothosaurs retreated hastily, swimming off in search of fishes and left the ichthyosaur family alone.

Ichthyosaurs were strange fish-like reptiles which gave birth to live young about 30 cm long. Preserved ichthyosaur skin revealed the dorsal fins and enabled scientists to work out its colour from the pigment cells.

Huge storms regularly swept across the ocean, breaking along the coasts, and the nothosaurs were forced to shelter in the depths of the sea-caves or climb up onto the land. One day, however, Andrian and his growing family were caught out in the open sea during a particularly violent storm. They were swept towards a group of islands across narrow straits separating the ocean waters from those of a shallow, clear inland sea. The nothosaurs sheltered in the lee of one of the islands and were able to rest in a cave. When the storm had passed they found other nothosaurs along the shores of the islands and they joined with these, establishing a new colony.

In the region of southwest Poland there was a string of islands across the straits separating the ancient ocean of Tethys from the shallow, clear Muschelkalk Sea of southern Germany and eastern France. There is evidence of violent storms in Triassic rocks in Poland, where beach gravels have been swept into caves, completely filling them. Dragonflies, beetles and cockroaches have all been found in Triassic rocks in Germany.

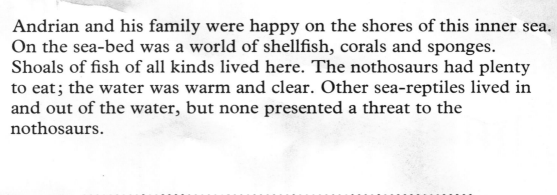

Andrian and his family were happy on the shores of this inner sea. On the sea-bed was a world of shellfish, corals and sponges. Shoals of fish of all kinds lived here. The nothosaurs had plenty to eat; the water was warm and clear. Other sea-reptiles lived in and out of the water, but none presented a threat to the nothosaurs.

As well as the sponges, corals and shellfish, two types of armoured reptile, placodonts, have been found in the region of the Muschelkalk Sea. They developed large, flat crushing teeth for feeding on the shellfish. Fossils have revealed that the primitive fish which swam in Triassic seas had a backbone which turned up at the tail end.

In time, the young were able to fend for themselves, and Andrian, on his own once more, swam northwest as strong currents swept across the sea. Eventually he reached a shore covered in thick vegetation. Here were swampy, humid forests with many fishes, amphibians and insects. Gliding lizards parachuted down from the trees, and small dinosaurs fed on the foliage. Andrian moved further northwestwards along the coast, and gradually the dense, tropical vegetation began to thin out.

The coastline was dominated by forests of the primitive conifer, *Voltzia,* rather like the monkey puzzle tree. There were abundant ferns, clubmosses and horsetails. Among the trees were gliding lizards, *Icarosaurus,* with a skin membrane stretched over long ribs that could be folded back when walking. Herbivorous dinosaurs, such as the *Thecodontosaurus,* have also been found in Germany and southwest England.

Now the landscape was much less swampy. There were wide open lagoons with vegetation around the edges. Andrian met herbivorous rhynchosaurs digging up roots with their bony beaks. There was abundant food and there were few enemies, occasional packs of flesheaters, but when they appeared Andrian was able to escape quickly into the water. The lagoons were full of fish and sometimes he caught a large, flat, newt-like *Gerrothorax,* which breathed by means of soft external gills. There were few other nothosaurs and no caves or other sheltered places, where they could bring up their young.

In the Middle Triassic period the sea spread from what is now Germany through Holland to England where there had previously been desert. Large, armoured amphibians have been found in the midlands of England, and a few two-legged flesh-eating dinosaurs, *Ornithosuchus,* have been found in Scotland. The first known tortoise, *Proganochelys,* which had teeth, was found in this period.

But the water in the lagoons began to get shallower and shallower. The muddy expanses dried out, and the ground became broken with deep mud cracks. Small lizards scuttled across the muds and sands. Andrian saw the large, squat armoured amphibian, *Mastodonsaurus*, and the flesheater *Cheirotherium* wandering over the landscape in search of prey. He could still find a few fish in the shrinking pools but the water was becoming stagnant. As the lagoons dried up, crusty salt deposits formed along the edges of the water. Andrian knew instinctively he could not survive long in this environment and he must turn and head back towards the sea. But the landscape over which he had travelled had changed. Large lagoons were now only tiny pools, the ground was dried mud and hot sand. He dragged himself on, trying to reach the open sea.

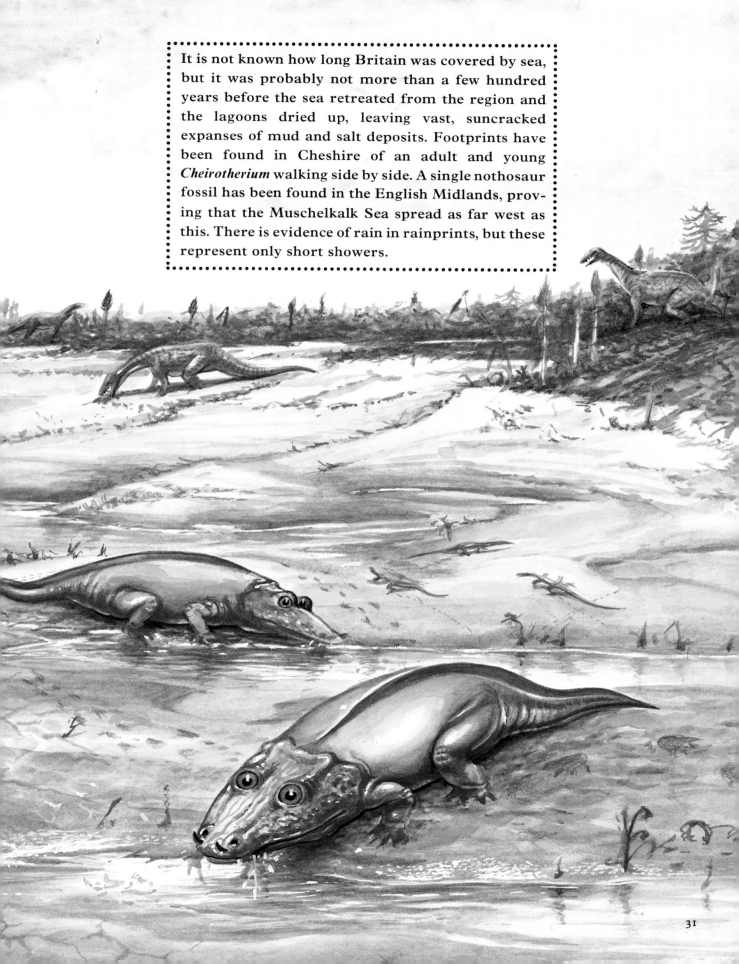

It is not known how long Britain was covered by sea, but it was probably not more than a few hundred years before the sea retreated from the region and the lagoons dried up, leaving vast, suncracked expanses of mud and salt deposits. Footprints have been found in Cheshire of an adult and young *Cheirotherium* walking side by side. A single nothosaur fossil has been found in the English Midlands, proving that the Muschelkalk Sea spread as far west as this. There is evidence of rain in rainprints, but these represent only short showers.

At last Andrian could see the sea on the horizon, but there was still a vast plain of dried muds and salts to cross. The fierce sun and hunger weakened him. There were dark clouds over the sea, moving closer. A few drops fell and he struggled over the mud. It was difficult to lift his feet. He slumped into the mud exhausted, and felt the cool rain on his hot skin as his strength finally drained away.